A MESSAGE TO PARENTS

It is of vital importance for parents to read good books to young children in order to aid the child's psychological and intellectual development. At the same time as stimulating the child's imagination and awareness of his environment, it creates a positive relationship between parent and child. The child will gradually increase his basic vocabulary and will soon be able to read books alone.

Brown Watson has published this series of books with these aims in mind. By collecting this inexpensive library, parent and child are provided with hours of pleasurable and profitable reading.

Teddy
at School

by Maureen Spurgeon
Illustrated by Pamela Storey

Brown Watson
ENGLAND

It was a beautiful day and Billy and Bella Bear had been playing with Teddy in his back garden. They had splashed in the paddling pool. They had played ball and Hide-and-Seek. Now, they were happy just to sit in the warm sunshine, nibbling biscuits, drinking squash and chatting to each other.

Suddenly, Billy said: "We won't be doing this tomorrow!"

"Or the next day!" added Bella, biting on a biscuit.

"Or the day after!" Billy went on. "We'll be at school!"

"I'm going to school tomorrow!" cried Teddy. "Mummy Bear's bought me a satchel and a lunch-box and a pencil-case, and . . ."
"Poor you!" said Bella.
"Never mind!" added Billy.

Teddy blinked. He had been with Mummy and Daddy Bear to see Teacher Bear's school. It seemed a very nice place to be.

"Why?" he asked at last. "What's wrong with school?"

"No sweets!" said Bella.
"You can't take any toys!" added
Billy. "Or talk to your friends! And,
as for school dinners . . ."
"YUK!" shuddered Bella.

Just then, Billy and Bella's daddy came to take them home, so Teddy couldn't ask any more questions about school. He had really thought he would like it. Now, he wasn't sure.

Mummy saw how worried Teddy was. "You'll love Teacher Bear's School," she said. "Just wait and see!" Teddy felt better then. Mummy Bear never said anything that wasn't true.

Next morning, Mummy packed Teddy's lunch-box. "No sweets, Teddy," she said. "Teacher Bear doesn't like them being brought to school."

Teddy Bear pulled a face.

"Cheer up!" smiled Mummy. "You can have an apple and some crisps, instead."
"Put that toy down, Teddy!" called Daddy Bear. "Then we'll be on our way."

"No sweets. No toys. That's what Billy and Bella told me," thought Teddy with a sigh.

"Hello, Teddy!" a voice called. It was Barrie Bear, one of Teddy's best friends.

Teddy waved and smiled.
"You'll see Barrie at playtime," said
Daddy Bear. "He's older than you,
Teddy, so he won't be in your
class." Teddy didn't like the sound
of that.

"Teddy Bear!" came a voice. "Lovely to see you!" It was Teacher Bear. "Hang your coat on this peg, the one with the picture of an engine. Do you like engines?" Teddy nodded.

"Then I want you to help Barbara feed the goldfish," Teacher Bear went on.

Barbara Bear smiled at Teddy. "I'll show you what to do, Teddy," she said.

Then Teddy sat at the table next to Honey Bear, while the drawing things were being given out. Barrie Bear's mummy was there too, sorting out lids from jam pots and coffee jars.

Soon Teddy was drawing round the lids, making a picture of a lovely bunch of balloons!
"I'm going to draw lots of trees!" said Tiny Bear. "Will you help me please, Teddy?"

And when all the lunch-boxes were opened, nobody minded about not having any sweets. "Teacher Bear says fruit and crisps are better for your teeth," explained Barrie Bear.

There was time for games in the playground, too.
Teddy loved climbing up the steps of the slide into a little hut, crawling through and then sliding down the other side.

Later on, he filled lots of paper cups with sand from the sand tray, ready to weigh them on the classroom scales. And what a lovely smell there was, coming from the school kitchen!

"Dinner time!" called Teacher Bear, ringing a little bell.
"Cheese and tomato pizza!" cried Teddy, sniffing hungrily. And he ate every bit, followed by some cool strawberry jelly.

After dinner, Teddy's class went into the play room. What toys there were! Puzzles and bricks, tricycles, push-along toys, balls, trains . . . There was no need to bring toys from home!

Teddy and his new friends had just finished a big jigsaw when Teacher Bear clapped her hands.
"Storytime!" she cried. "Put away the toys, then we'll go back to the classroom."

Teacher Bear had a lovely, big story-book with lots of pictures for everyone to see. Then they sang songs and nursery rhymes, clapping their hands in time to the music.

And when Teacher Bear said it was
time to go home, Teddy thought
about all the things he had done.
He remembered the lovely dinner
and the fun he'd had with his new
friends.

"Why did you say that you didn't like school?" he asked Billy on the way home.
"We said there were no sweets!" grinned Billy. "And that's true!"